AN ESSEX BOO1

In which Essex town would Peter Pan have been at home?
Front cover: Where is this figure – and what is she wearing?
Back cover: Who and where is this figure? And what is the purpose of the object in his hand?

Jill Howard-Jones

Illustrations by Helen Fenton

S.B. Publications

By the same author
A Herefordshire Quiz Book
Secret Hereford
A Cambridgeshire Quiz Book
A Suffolk Quiz Book

For Ray, Reg, Veronica and Gary

First published in 2000 by S. B. Publications,
19 Grove Road, Seaford, East Sussex BN25 1TP

ISBN 1 85770 188 7

Designed and typeset by CGB, Lewes
Printed by MFP Design and Print
Longford Trading Estate, Thomas Street,
Stretford, Manchester. M32 0JT.

CONTENTS

INTRODUCTION

WHERE do you start with Essex? It is a county of so many contrasts. Its history moves from the death of an East Saxon hero at the Battle of Maldon to the creation of a nuclear war bunker, now a public exhibit. Its geography is equally diverse. Land near the coast is flat and marshy but woodland is prolific in the south west. Industrial dockland hugs the Thames but natural beauty further north gave Constable a landscape to capture in oils.

I have tried to reflect the county's versatility in this quiz book, for Essex is an old friend. Visits to Southend-on-Sea featured in my childhood but my real introduction began when I married the curate of All Saints', Hutton who was ordained in Chelmsford cathedral and whose parents lived in Grays. I taught at St John's School, Billericay before our elder son was born at Brentwood. We later moved to Frinton, thence to Colchester.

So I think I know Essex, but how well do I or you, whether inhabitant or visitor, really know it? Not well enough, I suspect to answer all the questions in this book. That is why many are worded in such a way that they can be entertainingly guessed, while at the same time being unobtrusively informative.

'Who spent his boyhood at Gestingthorpe and later walked out into a blizzard to save his friends?' may well call to mind Scott of the Antarctic's brave friend. While 'an Essex island with equine associations' sounds distinctly Horsey.

I hope this quiz book will entertain families and groups in addition to the individual reader, with its competitive rounds, which may be chosen at random.

Answers at the back may be quickly found.

It has been fun to write. I hope it will be fun to read.

Jill Howard-Jones

1 RECORDS

1 Which is Britain's oldest recorded town?

2 Which town has the longest pleasure pier in the world?

3 What is Greensted church made of and why is it remarkable?

4 Where is the LARGEST Norman keep in England?

5 Where is the FINEST Norman keep in England?

6 What is the most famous village in Essex – and the most photographed?

7 What record is held by Oldfield Grove, Langley?

8 In which century was the earliest nunnery founded in Essex?

9 Which are the highest hills in Essex?

10 What record is held by Waltham Abbey?

2 STATELY HOMES

Empty lodgings. And unfurnished walls,
Unpeopled offices, untrodden stones.

Of Pleshey Castle, after the Duke of
Gloucester's murder in Shakespeare's
Richard II.

1 Which building stands next to Rainham Hall, to make a typical
   pair of Essex neighbours?

2 Why did neither Sir Henry Marney, nor his son get no further than
   building the gatehouse of their home at Layer Marney?

3 Why was the splendid timber-framed Paycockes in Coggeshall
   given to a butcher's son?

4 Audley End was the largest house in England when it was built in
   James I's reign by one of his ministers. Which one?

5 How does Gosfield Hall show that its builder Sir John Wentworth,
   had no confidence in Tudor law?

6 Daisy, Countess of Warwick, who lived at Little Easton Lodge, was
   a renowned hostess of the Edwardian era. Who was her royal lover?

7 What was Bourne Mill, Colchester, before it became a mill?

8 What once stood on the mound in the middle of Rayleigh Town?

9 Which King Henry of England gave permission for Faulkbourne
   Hall to be fortified?

10 Which King Henry of England built New Hall, Boreham which,
   next to Audley End, is the biggest old building in the county?

3 MEN OF NOTE

Chief Postmaster of Greate Britaine and foreign parts, second to none for unfathomed policy, unparalleled, sagacious, and divining genius; witness his great correspondence in all parts of the Christian World.

Epitaph at Hornchurch to Thomas Witherings who started the Post Office and distribution of letters for Charles I. He died on his way to a service at Hornchurch in 1651.

1 Why, in spite of his evil reputation, did Felsted honour Richard Rich with a huge monument in the parish church?

2 Robert Devereux, Earl of Essex, 1567-1601, is famous for being the favourite of which monarch?

3 What office did brothers Cedd and Chad both hold in the Church? 'A rare thing to be met with' according to the Venerable Bede.

4 In which town did Christopher Jones, Master of the *Mayflower*, live?

5 Who were the 'Earls' of Earls Colne?

6 He was the first president of the United States but his great-great-grandfather was ejected from his living at Purleigh and lies in an unknown grave at Maldon. Who was he?

7 Who spent his boyhood at Gestingthorpe and later walked out into a blizzard to save his friends ?

8 Who, in 1805, spoke the words: 'Thank God I have done my duty,' to Alexander Scott, later vicar of Southminster?

9 The founder of Pennsylvania was a pupil at Chigwell school. Who was he?

10 Who trained for the ministry in the house of a pastor at Chipping Ongar before setting out on his life's work in Africa in 1844?

4 WOMEN OF NOTE

'Let tyrants fear . . . I know I have the body of a weak and feeble woman, but I have the heart and stomach of a king, and a king of England too; and think foul scorn that Parma or Spain or any prince of Europe should dare to invade the borders of my realm'.

Elizabeth I to her troops at Tilbury on the approach of the Armada, 1588.

1 Which abbess had precedence over all the others in Essex?

2 How many husbands did Martha Blewitt of Birdbrook bury before she died in 1681?

3 Why is Pocahontas, the first North American Indian to become a Christian, buried in Gravesend churchyard?

4 With which queen did Henry VIII stay in Green Street House, East Ham?

5 The notorious Mrs Masham of High Laver was very influential at the court of which queen?

6 How did Lady Warwick of Easton Lodge show her love for animals in the late nineteenth century?

7 Which famous actress and great friend of Lady Warwick is remembered in a portrait in little Easton Church?

8 How did Hester Woodley, a black African who died in 1767 come to be buried at Little Parndon?

9 Frances Rich of Maldon was allowed by her father to marry Thomas Cammocke because 'she had ventured her life for him'. What did she do?

10 Who was the Quaker from Barking who roused Parliament into action over conditions in prisons?

5 WRITERS

'We should then be well in those long reaches below Gravesend, between Kent and Essex, where the river is broad and solitary, where the waterside inhabitants are very few, and where lone public-houses are scattered here and there, of which we could choose one for a resting-place'.

Charles Dickens. *Great Expectations.*

1 Which play did Shakespeare base on Cunobelin, who established a Romanized capital at Colchester?

2 What did Joseph Conrad think of his house in Stanford-le-Hope when he moved there in 1897?

3 Which Dickens' novel features the Lobster Smack, Hole Haven near Canvey Island?

4 Richard Church's essays written near Cole End, Wimbish have a fitting agricultural title. What is it?

5 What aspect of Shakespeare's England does William Harrison, Rector of Radwinter concentrate on in his book, *A Description of England?*

6 Nicholas Udall of Braintree wrote *Ralph Roister Doister*. It was the first of its kind, but what type of work was it?

7 How did Arthur Golding of Belchamp St Paul help Shakespeare?

8 Which writer called Chigwell 'the greatest place in the world' in his novel *Barnaby Rudge?*

9 Which author worked in Tilbury – allegedly in a tile factory, which perhaps made him fantasise about being alone on a desert island?

10 What was the profession of Philip Morant, author of *The History of Essex?*

6 POETS

'My soul, sit thou a patient looker-on;
Judge not the play before the play is done:
Her plot hath many changes; every day
Speaks a new scene: the last act crowns
the play.'

Francis Quarles, *Epigram. Respice Finem.*

1 Name the poet whose Prioress learnt her French at Stratford Abbey.

2 What well known nursery rhyme did Jane and Ann Taylor of Colchester write?

3 Which remarkable old English poem is based on a battle between the Saxons and Danes at an Essex port?

4 Tennyson's New Year verses, *Ring out the old, Ring in the new,* were inspired by the bells of which Essex abbey?

5 Which dramatist used an ancient king of Essex for the title of one of his blank verse plays?

6 Which English saint's life was translated by Alexander Barclay, Rector of Great Baddow, the scholar poet?

7 By which sixteenth century poet was Gabriel Harvey of Saffron Walden immortalised as Hobbinol in *The Shepherd's Calendar*?

8 Rainham's curate in 1756, Charles Churchill, was both a poet and satirist. William Cowper and the actor David Garrick commented on his work. What did they think of it?

9 Which famous poet, according to Horace Walpole, 'was forced to wait till the world had done admiring Quarles'? Francis Quarles, born in Romford in 1592, was the most popular serious English poet of his time.

10 Which Poet Laureate lived at High Beech, Epping?

7 VILLAGES OF NORTH AND CENTRAL ESSEX

'The time draws near the birth of Christ;
The moon is hid, the night is still;
A single church below the hill
Is pealing, folded in the mist.'
Tennyson. *In Memoriam.*

1 Add a little water to wings and you have the name of this village.

2 What building does Little Maplestead share with only two other places in the country?

3 Little Chesterford has the oldest manor house in Essex. In which century was it built?

4 What does 'Pleshey' mean ?

5 Which Essex villages are named after a Christian festival – one good, the other high?

6 How many Hanningfield villages are there in Essex?

7 Pebmarsh has a rare fourteenth century brass featuring Sir William Fitzralph. What is unusual about the position of his legs, and on what do his feet rest?

8 Why is Belchamp St Paul so called?

9 To what does Tollesbury allegedly owe its name?

10 A man coughing at Writtle heard on a hilltop in Kent announced the birth of which great British institution?

8 VILLAGES OF SOUTH AND CENTRAL ESSEX

'Caesar, when he made no secret to profess that he had rather be first in a village than second at Rome.'

Bacon, *Advancement of Learning.*

1 What stern reminder of law and order, with its tiny barred windows, stands near Hall Farm, Orsett?

2 What came down burning from a height of 8,000 feet into Great Burstead churchyard in 1916?

3 How do we know that East Tilbury was the forging centre to which the potters of Roman Britain brought their wares ?

4 In whose garden at East Hanningfield can you find the oldest well in Essex?

5 Between which two rivers is the large village of Southminster?

6 Which village bears an appropriate name for housing a medieval Marriage Feast Room?

7 Who made Chadwell's dene-holes?

8 It is described by Arthur Mee as 'Southend's mother village.'

9 Who or what is Margaret Roding?

10 How did Mucking get its name?

9 FOOD AND DRINK

'He had often eaten oysters, but had never had enough'.
W S Gilbert. *The 'Bab' Ballads, Etiquette.*

1 Which town contains the only works in the country producing crystalline salt from seawater?

2 Name one of the main species of fish caught in the Blackwater Estuary.

3 In which town would you find the Chicago Rock Café, Churchills, Yates Wine Lodge and Irish themed bars?

4 Which Essex town is famous for its jam?

5 For what seafood is West Mersea famous?

6 Why is the Maldon area often referred to as 'the bread basket of England'?

7 Who goes 'bananas' in Colchester?

8 When local farmer, John Webb, built Thaxted Windmill in 1804, for which substance (now associated with whisky) did he meet the demand ?

9 In which village church can you find the 'bacon chair' ?

10 'Boiled and raw oysters, chickens, a leg of pork, a sirloin of beef, a goose, veal, rabbits, soles, partridges, five sorts of pie, two puddings and an apple pie' plus unspecified quantities of beer and wine mixed with sugar were the items on a bill for a dinner served at the Blue Boar in Maldon in 1625. For how many people ?

10 FLOWERS AND TREES

'There rolls the deep where grew the tree,
O, Earth,what changes thou hast seen.'
Tennyson,

1 Which flower, cultivated as a dye and for medicine is carved into an arch in Saffron Walden church?

2 What kind of Holly and Lavender grow in the Dengie Coastal Area?

3 It was called the Forest of Essex, then the Forest of Waltham but what is its more well known name today?

4 In Chignal Smealey church, the glass leaves of which tree are the oldest things in the village?

5 Who was responsible for the rotten timbers that caused the sinking of the Royal George off Portsmouth in 1782?

6 How long ago is it since the trees that form the walls of Greensted's Saxon Church first grew in the forest? Approximately 500, 1,000, 1,500 or 2,000 years ago?

7 Goldhanger on the Blackwater estuary takes its name from which yellow flower?

8 Which biblical tree is depicted colourfully in the east window of Margaretting church?

9 William Coys of North Ockendon in the early seventeenth century was noted among contemporary botanists for a list that he made. What did he list?

10 A little ring of trees in Hempstead was known as Turpin's Ring. Why was it so called and for what was it thought to have been used?

11 INNS

1 What happened to Horndon farmer, Thomas Higbed behind the Bell Inn, Horndon-on-the-Hill in 1555 ?

2 What is unusual about the inn sign at the Plough, Radwinter?

3 How did the Short Blue Inn in Bastalde Avenue, Barking get its name?

4 An inn sign at Steeple Bumpstead shows a fox safe along the branch of a tree while the dogs go by in full cry below – so what is the name of the pub?

5 Which famous inn in Saffron Walden was said to be the headquarters of the Parliamentary forces in the Civil War?

6 Who wrote in the Saracen Inn, Chelmsford rather than in the cathedral close which would have been more appropriate for his novels?

7 Which inn, called after the industry which brought wealth to Coggeshall, would Thomas Paycocke have passed on his way to his famous house?

8 Which town has three ancient inns – the White Horse, the Blue Boar and the Bell?

9 In which of these three villages to the north east of Saffron Walden, (a) Hadstock (b) Bartlow (c) Ashdon, are there original wall paintings in its seventeenth century inn – the Rose and Crown?

10 It is blue with golden hoof, tusks and bristles and the insignia of John de Vere, Earl of Oxford. Name the inn and the town in which it can be found.

12 CREATURES

'That roasted Manningtree ox with the pudding in his belly.'
Prince Hal of Falstaff in Shakespeare's *King Henry IV, Part 1.*

1 A strange corbel on Abbess Roding church features a long white tongue, the mane of one animal and the snout of another. What creatures are involved?
2 Which creature adorns the lamp standards on the bridge across the River Pant at Bocking?
3 Which famous animal in London Zoo gave its name to Colchester's huge water tower?
4 Which horned creature's head is on the gable end of Hornchurch church?
5 It is stone and has a dead face framed between its paws. You can see it in Colchester Museum. What is it?
6 The ancient fountain at Mistley is in the shape of what creature?
7 Prince Charles, it is said, takes his everywhere. Its fellows can be found in Sir Isaac's walk, Colchester. What is it?
8 Name an Essex 'island' with equine associations.
9 After which beast is Colchester's shopping centre called?
10 What was the famous horse of Essex's famous highwayman called?

13 RIVERS

1 Which river flows from Broxted to Barking Creek and on the way gives its name to eight villages?

2 On which river does Essex's cathedral city stand?

3 Its estuary forms the southern boundary of Essex.

4 Which river flows by Burnham and Fambridge?

5 Which river was originally known as the Pant?

6 From which river does the oldest and most important town in Essex derive its name?

7 In which river valley stands Saffron Walden?

8 What is Pod's Brook's 'intellectual' name?

9 In which river estuary is Osea Island?

10 Which river winds its way through Romford, then joins the Beam and finally the Thames?

14 INDUSTRY AND AGRICULTURE

'*Tusser, they tell me when thou wert alive,
Thou teaching thrift, thyself couldst never thrive;
So, like the whetstone, many men are wont
To sharpen others when themselves are blunt*'.

Of Thomas Tusser of Fairstead, whose efforts to test his 500 points of good husbandry, met with little success.

1 Which town is known for its Ford Motor Works?

2 What is the world's largest shoe manufacturing and retailing group whose factory in East Tilbury was built in the 1930s?

3 Domes and pinnacles were said to sparkle and glow at Coryton by the Thames twenty years ago. What were they?

4 Why was one third of Canvey Island let to Danish farmers?

5 What were the two great barns at Cressing built by the Knights Templar intended to hold?

6 What is Hedingham ware?

7 With which ancient industry is Halstead associated?

8 Why was alcohol the reason for a chapel being built at Halstead?

9 What did Francis Crittal of Braintree invent and manufacture as the result of his mother injuring herself opening a window?

10 In which Essex city is Marconi's factory preserved and why ?

15 TRANSPORT

*'The whole of the back of the coach had been taken by a family
removing from London and there were no places for the two
prisoners but on the seat in front, behind the coachman'.*
Charles Dickens. *Great Expectations.*

1 George Shillibeer of Chigwell ran the first buses in London. How
   many horses were needed to pull each bus carrying twenty two
   passengers ?

2 How many years of railway history are covered by the East Anglia
   Railway Museum in Chappel Station, Colchester?

3 What happens on Cabbies Day in Maldon?

4 Through which river valley does a steam railway run from Castle
   Hedingham?

5 From which Italian city does a bridge in Clacton take its name?

6 In which part of Colchester is Nunn's Road ?

7 Which town is situated at the lowest bridge point of the Blackwater
   and the Chelmer ?

8 Name London's third airport, which is in Essex.

9 What is the early fifteenth century bridge at Pleshey Castle made of?

10 Which bridge on the River Crouch reflects the conflict between
    Edmund Ironside and Canute ?

16 SCIENTISTS AND BENEFACTORS

'Gilberd shall live till loadstones
cease to draw'.

John Dryden.

1 Of which subject was Gilberd's *De Magnete* of 1600 the first important study?

2 William Gilberd amused Elizabeth I with his experiments but what kind of experiments were they?

3 Who carried out his early experiments in radio telegraphy in Chelmsford?

4 Who discovered the circulation of the blood and was buried in Hempstead church in 1657?

5 Which science made John Ray of Black Notley, author of the seventeenth century *Historia Plantarium*, famous?

6 Dr Benjamin Allen, whose table tomb stands next to John Ray's obelisk at Black Notley is said to have cured Ray from jaundice, using a potion. What was the potion made from?

7 What did Lionel Luckin demonstrate on Doctor's Pond, Great Dunmow in 1785 which greatly contributed to the saving of human life at sea?

8 Henry Winstanley who worked for the Earl of Suffolk at Audley End, designed the first Eddystone lighthouse at Plymouth. How did he and his lighthouse both end their days?

9 What did Charles Haddon Spurgeon of Kelvedon write which cost a penny each and were translated into many languages?

10 Who was the Barkingside doctor who established homes for homeless children a century before State institutions offered shelter?

17 MILITARY MATTERS

'1016. The host went back into Essex . . . When the king learnt that the host had appeared on the scene, then for the fifth time he called up all the people of England and followed them up, overtaking them in Essex at the hill called Ashingdon, and there a fierce battle was fought'.
The Anglo Saxon Chronicles.

1 By what name with mineral associations is the fort built by Gordon of Khartoum in 1869 at East Tilbury known?

2 What did Admiral Walton do in 1718 to deserve his monument in Stockwell church?

3 Who defeated King Edmund Ironside at Ashingdon in 1016?

4 With which two counties did the Essex Regiment amalgamate to form the 3rd East Anglian Regiment in 1958?

5 What evidence of the Civil War can still be seen on the exterior of Siege House in East Street, Colchester?

6 Why did American servicemen stationed locally fire machine-gun bullets at the stone column in Colne Park at Colne Engaine?

7 What remnant of the Cold War can be found at Mistley?

8 Name the ferocious queen who destroyed Colchester in AD 60.

9 For what was Walton-on–the-Naze's beacon tower adapted for use during the Second World War?

10 A Tyrell of East Horndon fought at Agincourt. With whom did he fight and for which king?

18 TOWNS OF NORTH AND CENTRAL ESSEX

'*921. Before Martinmas, King Edward went with West Saxon levies to Colchester and repaired and rebuilt the fortress where it had been destroyed*'.

The Anglo Saxon Chronicles.

1 Which Colchester Museum is concerned exclusively with time?

2 What connection has the Celtic war god Camulos with Colchester?

3 How many thousands of years old is the Dagenham Idol in Colchester's Castle Museum?

4 It is in Wivenhoe Park and admitted its first students in 1964. What is it?

5 What role did Falcon Square play in the history of Castle Hedingham?

6 Which quality is personified on Braintree's town hall?

7 It is the oldest in Essex, built before Eddystone and now turned into a residence above the mile long promenade. What and where is it?

8 How did Saffron Walden get its name?

9 Jumbo dominates Colchester – but what is Jumbo?

10 Brightlingsea's Jacob's Hall is one of the oldest timber-framed buildings in England. In which century was it built?

19 TOWNS OF SOUTH AND CENTRAL ESSEX

'The East Saxons and the Ship-army
beset the River Panta in proud array.
Then Byrhtnoth, guardian of his men,
ordered
A warrior to defend the ford'.
The Battle of Maldon.

1 The Hythe was a separate hamlet serving Maldon as a port, so what did 'hythe' mean in Anglo-Saxon?

2 Ilford boasts a rare pillar box. Which monarch's cypher appears on it?

3 What has the Mayflower to do with Billericay?

4 What can you do at the Royals in Southend-on-Sea ?

5 What has been refurnished in the style of 1865 to delight children in Barking's Eastbury House Museum?

6 Which town on the River Roche was a family seat of the Earls of Warwick ?

7 Which is the largest town in the Dengie Hundred and an important yachting centre?

8 Which town derives it name from Elizabeth I's comment, 'Oh, my poor fleet!' as she watched the little ships sail down the Thames to tackle the Armada?

9 Which town is usually the first to announce its result at general elections ?

10 In which town is the church known as the Cathedral of the Dengie?

20 THE ARTS IN ESSEX

'Have nothing in your houses that you do not know to be useful, or believe to be beautiful'.

William Morris. *Hopes and Fears for Art.*

1 Who visited Hadleigh Castle in 1814 and captured the view later in a famous painting?

2 Which Colchester Theatre is called after a winged god?

3 Which town is known for its seafront illuminations from August to November?

4 How many times was James Waldegrave of Navestock's beautiful wife painted by Sir Joshua Reynolds?

5 Sarah Clark is remembered for her contribution to Pentlow's music. What did she play?

6 What is 42 feet long and celebrates the Battle of Maldon?

7 Gustav Holst, the celebrated composer lived in Town street, Thaxted. Which well known work did he draft there?

8 Which Essex town has the second oldest library in Britain?

9 Where might you be entertained in Bridge End Gardens, Saffron Walden by getting lost?

10 What kind of dancing regularly takes place in Thaxted on most bank holidays?

21 SPORT

'There is a passion for hunting something deeply implanted in the human breast'.

Charles Dickens. *Oliver Twist*

1 What sport has traditionally been associated with Epping Forest?

2 For what kind of sport is Tollesbury well known?

3 What is 'themed' at Clacton but available for more serious players at Millers Barn, Jaywick?

4 Which ball game enjoys a special week at Frinton in July?

5 Which town is often referred to as the 'Cowes of the East Coast'?

6 For what purpose can you hire shoes and balls in Cowdray Avenue, Colchester?

7 How many sailing clubs are there in Southend-on-Sea?

8 Dean Merivale, Rector of Lawford achieved a first in rowing. What did he do?

9 What kind of game is Quasar, played at Rollerworld in Colchester?

10 Who is based at Roots Hall, Southend?

22 ROYALTY

'Regions Caesar never knew,
Thy posterity shall sway.
Where his eagles never flew
None invincible as they'.

William Cowper. *Boadicea.*

1   Who came down the Thames to Tilbury on 8 August 1588 to review her troops?

2   Rare feather kings' cloaks from which tropical island are on show in the Saffron Walden Museum?

3   The body of Thomas Woodstock, Duke of Gloucester was brought back to Pleshey Castle to be buried. Who was the nephew and king who murdered him?

4   Why was Writtle, near Chelmsford a favourite haunt of King John?

5   According to legend, which animal appeared whenever Sighere King of the East Saxons tried to consummate his marriage with Queen Ostyth?

6   Which queen of England was the patient of royal physician, Sir Richard Blackmore of Boxted?

7   Which king built a church for Stigand at Ashingdon in AD 1020?

8   This young king put Sir Edward Waldegrave of Borley in the Tower; his stepsister bribed Waldegrave into approving her marriage to the Spanish king; and her stepsister imprisoned him for allowing mass to be said in his house. Name the three royals.

9   Saffron Walden treasures a glove worn by which tragic queen on the morning of her execution?

10 Who was the Dane who became one of the greatest English kings after his victory in Essex in 1016?

23 FOR ALL THE SAINTS

'I have never seen an ugly child'.
Dr. Barnardo of Barkingside.

1 Who made Mellitus Bishop of London so that he could convert the East Saxons in 604?

2 To which three saints is Chelmsford cathedral dedicated?

3 Which relative of St Cedd is probably wrongly associated with Chadwell?

4 Which order of monks was founded by King Stephen at Coggeshall Abbey?

5 How did the Reverend Arthur Pertwee of Brightlingsea show his concern for lost seamen?

6 Whose missionary church was at Tilaburg (probably East Tilbury) in 653?

7 Who was the saint of prisons from Barking?

8 Cressing Temple Barns, between Witham and Braintree were built by which order of warrior monks?

9 Who set sail for America from Harwich in 1620?

10 Who is the patron saint of Colchester?

24 CHURCHES

'Sleep at my bidding crept from pew to pew'.

Charles Churchill, a vicar of Rainham in the eighteenth century

1 What have the churches at Blackmore, Stock, Bobbingworth and Navestock in common?

2 Where in Feering church can you find Santa Claus?

3 To get the best out of Castle Hedingham church, should you look up, down or to left and right?

4 Why is there a watchbox in Wanstead churchyard ?

5 What characteristic of many Essex churches has been described as 'plain, massive even bald'?

6 Which is longer, Thaxted's spire or its church?

7 Which patron saint sits on a corner of Chelmsford cathedral in his sea boots, clutching an outsized Yale key?

8 Who ordered a church 'of stone and lime' to be built at Ashingdon in 1020 to celebrate the scene of his greatest victory?

9 What exploded in Navestock churchyard in 1940?

10 What is the primitive sign of Christianity found in mosaic in the chancel floor of East Tilbury church?

25 CRIME AND PUNISHMENT

*'To obey is better than sacrifice and
to hearken than the fat of rams.
For rebellion is as the sin of
witchcraft'.*
1 Samuel, xv 22

1 Matthew Hopkins, a seventeenth century lawyer of Manningtree was an avid witchhunter, but how did he himself die?

2 Who betrayed Bishop Fisher, Sir Thomas More, Thomas Cromwell, The Protector Somerset and Lady Jane Grey among others, but is revered in Felsted for founding a school?

3 Who was the Hempstead innkeeper's son turned highwayman?

4 How did a piece of skin (which can be seen by making an appointment with the vicar of Copford) act as a warning to criminals?

5 Against which king did Lord Scrope of Masham, Lord of Fyfield Manor, plot prior to the Battle of Agincourt?

6 Where did Sir Thomas Malory, author of *Morte d'Arthur*, suffer in prison?

7 What is the reason for the spiked tomb at Wanstead?

8 How much was John Norman fined for talking and swearing during the service at Tollesbury church?

9 When Elizabeth I rode into London as Queen, she denied only Edmund Bonner of Copford, Bishop of London the right to kiss her hand. What crime had he committed?

10 What two punishment aids were brought from Newport to be displayed outside Saffron Walden Museum?

26 TRADITION AND FOLKLORE

'The bacoun was nat fet for hem, I trowe,
That som men han in Essex at Dunmowe'.

Geoffrey Chaucer. *Canterbury Tales. The Prologue*
of the Wyves' Tale of Bathe.

1 To what ceremony was Chaucer referring in the above quote?

2 What did Essex lords traditionally build next to their halls?

3 The tradition that the seven large round barrows at Ashdon, on the Bartlow Hills, are the graves of heroes killed in battle between Canute and Edmund Ironside is incorrect. With which other place is Ashdon likely to have been confused?

4 Why will not grass grow round the obelisk at Colchester Castle, which commemorates two commanders?

5 Why did George Boote put a carved figure of a woman in a chastity belt on the corner of his house in Felsted?

6 What, according to legend, did much damage to crops and stock in the area round Bures Hamlet, until it was scared off by local archers?

7 What has the burn mark on the south door of St Mary's church, Runwell to do with the devil?

8 Why is Wormingford's 'Bloody Meadow' so called?

9 Why is mud to the fore in Maldon on New Year's Day or Boxing Day?

10 Why did the Devil of Stansgate take a man's plough?

27 ESSEX BY THE SEA

'For you dream you are crossing the Channel, and
tossing about in a steamer from Harwich –
Which is something between a large bathing machine
and a very small second class carriage.

W S Gilbert. *Iolanthe*

1 Which town has the second longest pier in Britain?

2 How many miles of sea front are occupied by Southend?

3 Which island did man win back from the sea and cover with bungalows?

4 Where can you see stars in Southend – in daylight?

5 From which historic port are Scandinavia and Holland just three and a half hours away by catamaran?

6 To what commodity did Burnham owe its success as a port in the Middle Ages?

7 How long is Southend Pier? Is it (a) one mile, (b) 1.27 miles, (c) 1.33 miles or, (d) 1.41 miles?

8 Which was the main port of Essex in medieval times ?

9 Why did the 'marshmen' of the Dengie coastal area on the Blackwater estuary start using decoy ponds?

10 Which Essex resort is known for its sophistication, glorious beach, Victorian beach huts and treelined avenues?

28 GHOSTS

'First I heard a thumping noise and then I saw the ghost. It was pure white and coming down the A13 from the direction of Vange Church and then it disappeared over in the direction of the Fobbing rail crossing.'.

John Howard, licensee of the Five Bulls Inn, as reported in the *Thurrock Gazette* on 26 September 1969.

1 What happened to Borley Rectory, reputedly the most haunted in England?

2 The fifteenth century evil priest Rainaldus of Runwell was seen several times in the 1950s. Was he wearing (a) clerical grey, (b) a black cape lined with red silk over his cassock, or (c) a brown robe?

3 Why did a cottage in Stock Road, Billericay take a long time to build?

4 Why was no-one able to sleep in Old Jarvis Hall Barn, Thundersley?

5 In what part of Copford Church, which he allegedly haunts, is the infamous Bishop Bonner said to be buried?

6 What kind of musical ghost were the Phenomenist Research League investigating in 1956 when they visited Bowers Gifford Church?

7 In the first half of the present century, the vision of a beautiful, saintly woman had apparently been frequently seen in All Saints, Middleton. Who was she believed to be?

8 What appeared in the sea, covered with sea shells and seaweed at Walton-on-the-Naze in January 1928 and was thought to be an apparition?

9 What did a hard-headed business man see in Braintree parish church in 1921?

10 What was the rational explanation for the strange lights on Pitsea marshes in the nineteenth century?

NORTH AND CENTRAL ESSEX
PICTURE QUIZ

The birthplace of Dick Turpin (1705)

1 Can you name the village – and the house?

2 On which town does this ruined Norman castle look down from Bury Hill?

3 Name this church with its memorial to Martha Blewit, who was outlived only by her ninth husband.

4 This Moot Hall stands in the centre of a village which has lost the steeple which gave it its name, so what is it called ?

5 Where are we – in reach of water and overlooked by a windmill?

6 The tallest gatehouse in Britain – but where is it?

7 In which Essex village is this smallest of England's three round churches?

8 What led to the rumour that this column in Colne Park was filled with liquid gold?

9 To which Essex zoo is this the entrance?

10 To which town does this fine Norman keep give its name?

SOUTH AND CENTRAL ESSEX
PICTURE QUIZ

1 Where is this picturesque quay?

2 Name the river – and the bridge.

3 What did they make in this seventeenth century boiling pan in Tiptree?

4   What is the black square to the left of the window facing the road in this former post office at Faulkbourne?

| 5 | Which well known seaside resort is this? |

| 6 | The view of which river valley – from which church – is this site of the battle in which Canute defeated Edmund Ironside in 1016? |

7 What came down at Little Wigborough on 24 September 1916? A part of it is pictured hanging in the church.

8 In which city church is this chapel to the Essex Regiment?

9   What hangs from the beam at the Bell, Horndon-on-the-Hill?

10 Name the inn displaying this sign at Little Dunmow.

ANSWERS

1 RECORDS

1 Colchester, the first capital of Roman Britain is the oldest town of which records exist in the country.

2 Southend-on-Sea. Its nineteenth century iron pier stretches for more than a mile and a quarter out to sea.

3 It is made of wood. It is the oldest surviving wooden church, probably built in the ninth century.

4 Colchester Castle (1078).

5 Castle Hedingham.

6 Finchingfield. The scene across the pond to the steep main street with the church beyond is a popular subject for photographers and artists.

7 It is the highest point in Essex – 482 feet, 147 metres.

8 Seventh century. Barking Abbey was founded in AD 675.

9 Laindon Hills.

10 It is reputedly the oldest Norman building in England.

2 STATELY HOMES

1 The church.

2 Sir Henry died, having completed only the gatehouse with its turrets of eight storeys and two fluted chimneys. His son died a year later, without an heir, so the house was never finished.

3 As a wedding present. Butcher John Paycocke built the house for his son, Thomas on his marriage to Margaret Horrold. Their initials T P and M P decorate the joists in the great chamber.

4 The Lord Treasurer. 'Too much for a king, but it might do very well for a Lord Treasurer', was James I's comment to Thomas Howard of Walden, Earl of Suffolk, creator of Audley End.

5 It has no windows at ground level, in case of attack, and a substantial gatehouse for protection against unwelcome visitors.

6 King Edward VII. The house at Little Easton was destroyed by fire.

7 A fishing lodge, built in 1591 and later converted into a mill. The waterwheel is still intact and the mill is open to the public on certain days in spring and summer. Tel: 01206 572422.

8 The Domesday Castle erected by Sweyn of Essex.

9 King Henry VI gave permission to its owner to fortify the fifteenth century hall.

10 Henry VIII whose arms are richly carved on its stone.

3 MEN OF NOTE

1 He founded Felsted public school.
2 Elizabeth I.
3 They both became bishops.
4 Harwich. His house forms part of the Harwich Maritime Trail.
5 Earls of Oxford, the de Veres of Castle Hedingham.
6 George Washington. Lawrence was his great-great grandfather.
7 Captain Oates, who went with Scott to the Antarctic.
8 Nelson. Alexander Scott was his chaplain on the *Victory*. After the battle of Trafalgar, Scott became Vicar of Southminster.
9 William Penn.
10 David Livingstone.

4 WOMEN OF NOTE

1 The Abbess of Barking.
2 Eight. The ninth survived. She is commemorated by a tablet in Birdbrook Church.
3 She died there, in 1617, before she could return home. She came to England to be presented to James I, after attending a missionary school.
4 Anne Boleyn.
5 Queen Anne.
6 No creature was allowed to be killed or hurt by human hand in her park and animals were allowed to come into her drawing-room.
7 Ellen Terry.
8 She was a slave. She belonged to Mrs Bridget until her mistress died and then worked for her daughter.
9 She eloped, and to escape from her irate father, had to leap into the estuary with her lover and swim half a mile against a strong tide. They reached Fambridge Ferry. The father relented at seeing their courage and allowed them to marry in All Saints, Maldon.
10 Elizabeth Fry.

5 WRITERS

1 *Cymbeline.*
2 Not much! He described it as a 'damned jerry-built rabbit hutch'.
3 *Great Expectations*, when Pip tries to smuggle his benefactor, the doomed convict, out of the country.

4 *Calling for a Spade*, published 1939.
5 The social life.
6 The first English comedy.
7 Golding translated the classics from which Shakespeare was then able to take many of his plots.
8 Charles Dickens.
9 Daniel Defoe, author of *Robinson Crusoe*.
10 A clergyman. He was the Rector of Aldham in the mid-eighteenth century.

6 POETS

1 Geoffrey Chaucer.
2 *Twinkle, twinkle little star.*
3 The Battle of Maldon.
4 Waltham Abbey.
5 William Shakespeare. *Cymbeline*
6 St George. Barclay also translated Brant's *Ship of Fools* into English verse.
7 Edmund Spenser. Harvey, now a forgotten poet, was at Pembroke College with Spenser.
8 They admired it, but had reservations it seems. Cowper described him as 'Great Churchill, with a certain rude and earth-born vigour'. Garrick added: 'Such talents, with prudence, had commended the nation'. Churchill's verse is now rarely read.
9 Milton, whose work lives on, while that of Quarles is now forgotten.
10 Alfred Lord Tennyson.

7 VILLAGES OF NORTH AND CENTRAL ESSEX

1 Birdbrook.
2 Its round church (built by the Knights Hospitallers).
3 Thirteenth century.
4 An enclosure. The whole of the original village is enclosed by an earthwork.
5 Good Easter and High Easter.
6 Three: East, South and West Hanningfield.

7 He is lying cross-legged, his feet resting on his hound.
8 Because it was given to St. Paul's Cathedral by Athelstan, first king of all England.
9 Tolls were thought to be levied there on ships sailing up the river (Blackwater Estuary).
10 The BBC. The coughing was heard on a crystal receiver in Kent.

8 VILLAGES OF SOUTH AND CENTRAL ESSEX

1 The village lock-up.
2 A Zeppelin – the second brought down in England.
3 Broken fragments of Samian ware were still being found in the mud well into the present century. Foundations of the ferrymen's huts are also authentic.
4 The vicar's. The well is 480 feet deep.
5 The Crouch and the Blackwater.
6 Matching. Mr Chimney set up a long building between the church and green with a room overhanging four lower rooms. The upper room was for wedding feasts.
7 The deep pits were probably dug by men looking for flints or were chalk mines or for grain stores. They are believed to go back to the Bronze Age.
8 Prittlewell.
9 A village, one of eight Rodings. The church dedicated to Margaret of Antioch gives this village its name.
10 Not from muck but from Mucca, a savage old pirate ancestor of the Saxons who settled there.

9 FOOD AND DRINK

1 Maldon. The Salt Works there continues the tradition of salt-making.
2 Any of the following: Thornback Rays, Bass, Eels, Flounders, Smoothounds, Stingray, Whiting and Cod.
3 Southend-on-Sea.
4 Tiptree. Wilkins of Tiptree, jam shop, tea room and museum open daily 10am-5pm. Monday to Saturday. Admission free. Tel: 01621 815407.

5 Oysters.
6 The River Blackwater in the Maldon area was and is still important for transporting grain.
7 Children between the ages of five and twelve. Go Bananas is a converted warehouse with a three storey play frame in Colchester.
8 Malt. The mill is open to the public. Tel: 01799 513779.
9 Little Dunmow. The winning couple of the Dunmow Flitch are carried in it through the streets before being presented with the flitch.
10 Three only. They were tax commissioners.

10 FLOWERS AND TREES

1 The saffron crocus.
2 Sea Holly and Sea Lavender. The latter covers large areas of this coastal area in summer.
3 Epping Forest.
4 Oak leaves and foliage appear in two windows of the church.
5 The Admiralty were responsible, through neglect.The font cover in Dedham church is made from some recovered timbers.
6 The oaks felled were growing 2,000 years ago.
7 The Corn Marigold. 'Hanger' refers to the grassland. The name Goldhanger appears in the Domesday Book
8 The tree of Jesse, the genealogical tree of David.
9 Garden plants. He made the first complete garden list with all the plants scientifically explained.
10 Dick Turpin was born at Hempstead. The ring was thought to be an enclosure for cock fights.

11 INNS

1 He was burnt to death in Mary Tudor's reign, condemned to suffer in his own parish.
2 It is a real plough.
3 From an eighteenth century fishing fleet based at Barking. The Short Blue Line was owned by a local family.
4 The Fox and Hounds.
5 The old Sun Inn in Castle street on the corner of Church street . It is no longer an inn.

6 Anthony Trollope who wrote the Barchester novels.
7 The Woolpack.
8 Maldon.
9 Ashdon.
10 The Blue Boar, Maldon.

12 CREATURES

1 A lion and a pig.
2 Dolphins. They were the first coat of arms of a parish council in 1926.
3 Jumbo, the elephant.
4 A bull.
5 The so-called Colchester Sphinx.
6 A swan. It is one of the oldest working fountains in Essex.
7 A teddy bear. The Bear Shop is in Colchester.
8 Horsey Island.
9 Lion (Walk).
10 Black Bess.

13 RIVERS

1 The Roding.
2 River Chelmer.
3 The Thames.
4 The Crouch.
5 The Blackwater.Its upper reaches known as the Pant was originally the name of the whole river.
6 The Colne (Colchester).
7 The Slade.
8 The Brain.
9 The Blackwater. The island is now privately owned.
10 The River Rom.

14 INDUSTRY AND AGRICULTURE

1 Dagenham.
2 (Thomas) Bata Shoes. It was set up in the former Czechoslovakia but has operations in sixty countries and employs 57,000 people.

3 The oil refineries of Thames Haven.
4 In return for the defences they built against the sea. Tiny octagonal cottages were then set up by the Dutch settlers.
5 One was for wheat, the other for barley.
6 Pottery.
7 The cloth trade in the sixteenth century, later replaced by the silk trade established originally at Pebmarsh by the Courtauld family.
8 It was kindly provided by the management of Fremlin's Brewery, within their premises.
9 The metal window frame : Crittall windows.
10 Chelmsford. Marconi's early experiments in radio telegraphy were carried out there.

15 TRANSPORT

1 Three horses.
2 A total of 150 years. The museum is open daily from 10 am-5pm.
3 A procession of colurfully decorated London taxis arrive in Maldon. Their drivers give handicapped children from the East End a day out every July.
4 The Colne Valley Railway 01787 461174.
5 Venice : the Venetian Bridge.
6 The Dutch Quarter.
7 Maldon.
8 Stansted.
9 Brick. It is probably the earliest brick bridge in Western Europe and unique in Britain.
10 Battlesbridge.

16 SCIENTISTS AND BENEFACTORS

1 Physics. Gilberd was also elected president of the College of Physicians.
2 He amused her with electrical experiments, but he was in fact her physician.
3 Marconi.
4 William Harvey.
5 Botany. He was famous for his *History of Plants*.

6 Horse dung and beer.
7 He demonstrated the world's first unsinkable lifeboat there.
8 The lighthouse was swept away in a storm in November 1703 and Winstanley with it.
9 His sermons.
10 Dr Thomas John Barnardo.

17 MILITARY MATTERS

1 The Coalhouse Fort (used in the First World War).
2 He destroyed the Spanish Fleet – off Cape Passaro in 1718.
3 Canute, in spite of the fact that 'all England fought against him', according to the *Anglo Saxon Chronicles*.
4 Bedfordshire and Hertfordshire.
5 Bullet holes, inflicted by the Roundheads who laid seige to the town in 1648.
6 The column was built by the architect J.Soane, designer of the Bank of England. A local had told them that it was filled with liquid gold.
7 The former County Nuclear War Bunker. Open to visitors Tel: 01206 392271.
8 Queen Boudica (Boadicea).
9 It carried a radar aerial.
10 Against the French, for Henry V.

18 TOWNS OF NORTH AND CENTRAL ESSEX

1 Tymperleys Clock Museum, Trinity Street, home to a fine selection of eighteenth and nineteenth century Colchester-made clocks.
2 Colchester was called after Camulos – its was originally Camulodunum – and its inhabitants were appropriately warlike.
3 It is 4,000 years old.
4 The University of Essex.
5 Falcon Square was originally the old market place.
6 The figure of Truth.
7 The lighthouse at Harwich.
8 From the local production of saffron.

9 A water tower built in 1882.

10 In the thirteenth century as a 'moot' or meeting place.

19 TOWNS OF SOUTH AND CENTRAL ESSEX

1 Landing place. Hythe Quay is still the maritime heart of Maldon.

2 Edward VIII's who abdicated in 1936.

3 The English group of Pilgrim fathers who sailed in the Mayflower, assembled there before embarking. Christopher Martin, Governor of the Mayflower came from Billericay.

4   Shop – beneath a glass dome.

5 A Georgian dolls' house.

6 Rochford. It was the home of the first Earl of Warwick.

7 Burnham-on-Crouch.

8 Purfleet.

9 Billericay.

10 Burnham-on-Crouch, St Mary's Church.

20 THE ARTS OF ESSEX

1 Constable. He captured the view of the ruined castle right on the edge of the escarpment with marshes and river gleaming below.

2 The Mercury.

3 Southend-on-Sea.

4 Seven.

5 The church organ – for sixty six years.

6 The Maldon Embroidery. For more information and opening hours ring Maldon Town Council on 01621 857373.

7 *The Planets Suite.*

8 Maldon.

9 The Hedge Maze.

10 Morris dancing. The famous Morris Ring attracts up to 300 dancers from all over the country on the first weekend after the Spring Bank holiday .

21 SPORT

1 Hunting, the royal sport of the Norman and Angevin kings.
2 Sailing. It has a large yacht harbour excavated from the saltings.
3 A golf course. There is a nine gole course at Jaywick.
4 Tennis. The Frinton Tennis Week is held in July.
5 Burnham-on-Crouch, because sailing is such a popular pastime throughout the year.
6 For bowling at the Superbowl.
7 Six and a motorboat club. Most offer temporary membership to visitors.
8 He rowed in the first university boat race.
9 A laser game set in a futuristic arena with players, from the age of eight upwards, tagging each other with laser guns.
10 Southend United Football Club.

22 ROYALTY

1 Queen Elizabeth.
2 Hawaii.
3 Richard II. The murder of his uncle marked the beginning of the collapse of his own power.
4 He had a hunting-lodge there.
5 A large and aggressive white stag. St Ostyth later entered a nunnery, became an abbess and died violently at the hands of pirates.
6 Queen Anne.
7 Canute built the church in 1020.
8 Edward VI, Mary and Elizabeth I.
9 Mary Stuart, Queen of Scots.
10 Canute.

23 FOR ALL THE SAINTS

1 St Augustine. Mellitus's mission was, however, a disaster and he had to escape overseas.
2 St Mary the Virgin, St Peter and St Cedd.
3 His brother, Chad, missionary to the Mercians. Cedd certainly visited the area around Chadwell, although Chad probably did not.
4 The Cistercians who, by tradition, preferred a lonely site near water.

5 He stood in the church tower on stormy nights with a lantern, guiding ships to safety. He also set up a display of plaques to lost seamen in his church.
6 St Cedd's. An old coffin slab in East Tilbury church was once said to be his but he actually died in Yorkshire.
7 Elizabeth Fry. She lived in Barking and is buried there.
8 The Knights Templar.
9 The Pilgrim Fathers.
10 St Helena, daughter of King Cole was born in Colchester and taken to Rome by the Roman general whom she married.

24 CHURCHES

1 Timber towers with shingled spires.
2 In a nineteenth century stained glass window which depicts the legend of St Nicholas or Santa Claus.
3 Up. Castle Hedingham has the most magnificent double-hammerbeam roof in Essex – and the great wheel window is also worth an admiring look.
4 This small stone shelter, more than 200 years old, was for a watchman to guard against grave robbers.
5 Norman towers.
6 The church by two feet. The spire is 181 feet.
7 St Peter.
8 Canute.
9 An enemy landmine. It exploded above ground when it caught in a tree and virtually destroyed the church. A sundial standing in the depression made by the explosion bears the inscription: 'An enemy landmine fell here on 21 November 1940'.
10 The fish.

25 CRIME AND PUNISHMENT

1 He was tried as a witch; he was 'swum' as a sorcerer; he floated and was hanged in 1647.
2 Richard Rich.
3 Dick Turpin.

4 Criminals used to be flayed and their skin nailed to the churchdoor as a warning to others. The piece in question is said to have been flayed from a Danish pirate.

5 Henry V. Shakespeare describes Scrope as that 'cruel, ingrateful, savage and inhuman creature'.

6 Colchester Castle.

7 The spikes were to ward off grave robbers (Resurrectionists) who exhumed newly buried bodies and sold them to medical students for research.

8 He was fined £5 and elected to buy the font for that amount instead of being prosecuted.

9 He was responsible for the deaths of 200 Protestants including bishops Latimer, Ridley and Cranmer.

10 Whipping post and pillory.

26 TRADITION AND FOLKLORE

1 The Dunmow Flitch. Since 1111 the Dunmow Flitch, a side of cured pork, can be claimed every four years by any couple proving to a jury they have not regretted their marriage within the year. Winners are few.

2 The church. The lord regarded the church as his personal province.

3 Ashingdon in the Crouch valley.

4 Because the commanders (Sir Charles Lucas and Sir George Lisle) were both shot there.

5 Figureheads on houses were supposed to keep out evil spirits....but the Hag of Felsted is probably his wife.

6 A dragon, *dente serrato*.

7 It is said to be the devil's clawed hand that marked the door. According to legend,the curate Rainaldus was practising Black Magic in the churchyard when the devil suddenly tried to grab him. The curate ran into the church and the devil, unable to enter the sanctified doorway, burned his mark on the door.

8 A dragon was killed there by Sir George de la Haye, the local lord, who according to legend thus saved the villagers.

9 The Maldon Mud Race takes place.

10 Because the man had angrily and unwisely said the Devil could have his soul if he would do the ploughing. The field is still called the Devil's Field.

27 ESSEX BY THE SEA

1 Walton-on-the-Naze.
2 Seven miles – from Crow Stone to Thorpe Bay.
3 Canvey Island. Not much is more than ten feet above sea level.
4 At the Planetarium, the only one in the South East outside London.
5 Harwich.
6 Wool.
7 (c) 1.33 miles.
8 Maldon.
9 To trap wild fowl. On star-shaped ponds tame ducks were used to lure the wild birds down to feed. They were then decoyed into netting pipes near the 'arms' of the star.
10 Frinton-on-Sea.

28 GHOSTS

1 It was burnt down.
2 All three – on different occasions.
3 Every morning the materials erected the previous day disappeared, allegedly by ghostly means.
4 The spirits of former inhabitants prevented anyone closing their eyes.
5 Under the High Altar.
6 The phantom organist.
7 St Mary the Virgin, to whom the church had been previously dedicated.
8 The 'ghost' church, swept away by the sea in 1798. It was visible for a few hours only, as the result of an exceptionally low tide before the sea covered it again.
9 A vision of Christ crucified.
10 Smugglers. Ghostly light can also be caused by the spontaneous combustion of gases from decaying vegetable matter on marshy ground.

29 NORTH AND CENTRAL ESSEX PICTURE QUIZ

1 Hempstead. The Bluebell Inn.
2 Saffron Walden.
3 Birdbrook church.
4 Steeple Bumpstead.
5 Finchingfield.
6 Layer Marney.
7 Little Maplestead.
8 It was built by the designer of the Bank of England, Sir John Soane.
9 Colchester Zoo.
10 Castle Hedingham. This finest Norman keep in Western Europe is open Easter to October 10am-5pm. At other times by appointment. Tel: 01787 460261.

30 SOUTH AND CENTRAL ESSEX PICTURE QUIZ

1 Hythe Quay, Maldon.
2 The River Crouch. Battlesbridge. The bridge gives its name to the place where the Danish ships are thought to have waited for the result of Canute's battle with Edmund Ironside.
3 Jam – in the Wilkin's jam factory at Tiptree. The spade is used like a spoon for stirring the boiling ingredients.
4 A little trapdoor so the postmaster in the days of horse-drawn mail vans need not get out of bed to receive the mail at 4am.
5 Southend-on-Sea.
6 The Crouch valley from St Andrews, Ashingdon.
7 A German Zeppelin.
8 St.Peter's Chapel in Chelmsford Cathedral.
9 Hot Cross buns. Traditionally the oldest regular drinker hangs a hot cross bun up every year.
10 The Flitch of Bacon.

COVER AND TITLE PAGE PICTURES

Front cover: In Felsted, on the George Boote House. The 'Hag of Felsted'
is wearing a chastity belt.

Title page: Southend-on-Sea, in the Never Never Land.

Back cover: St Peter, dressed as a modern fisherman, on a corner of
Chelmsford cathedral. He holds the key to heaven.

LINE DRAWINGS ON SPECIFIC SUBJECTS

Quiz
1 The Norman keep of Colchester Castle, built by Eudo Dapifer using
Roman materials.
2 Bourne Mill.
3 David Livingstone
4 Elizabeth Fry.
6 Francis Quarles.
7 Hempstead village sign.
8 Thaxted's old Guildhall.
9 Oysters.
10 Sea lavender.
11 Old Shambles hotel sign at Billericay.
12 Dolphin.
13 Harwich fishing boat.
14 Ford Eight
16 Bust of William Harvey.
18 Chelmsford's civic arms.
19 Maldon's civic arms.
22 Silver coin of King Canute.
23 Cressing Temple Barns.
24 Church of the Knights Hospitallers, Little Maplestead.
26 Dunmow Fltch chair.
27 Harwich lighthouse.

BIBLIOGRAPHY

Essex by Marcus Crouch.
Essex by Arthur Mee. King's England Series. Hodder and Stoughton.
A Ghost Hunter's Guide to Essex by Jessica K. Payne. Ian Henry Publications.
Timpson's England by John Timpson. Jarrold Publications.

ACKNOWLEDGEMENTS

My thanks to my husband, Ray, for his interest, helpful suggestions and driving skills in Essex. I would also like to record my thanks to the staff of the Tourist Information Centres in Colchester, Maldon, Saffron Walden and Southend on Sea.